LIFE
TOOLKIT

Outsmarting Bullies

Louise Spilsbury

raintree
a Capstone company — publishers for children

Raintree is an imprint of Capstone Global Library Limited, a company incorporated in England and Wales having its registered office at 264 Banbury Road, Oxford, OX2 7DY – Registered company number: 6695582

www.raintree.co.uk
myorders@raintree.co.uk

Produced for Raintree by Calcium Creative Ltd
Edited by Sarah Eason, Rachel Blount, and Robyn Hardyman
Designed by Paul Myerscough and Keith Williams
Media research by Rachel Blount
Original illustrations © Capstone Global Library Limited 2021
Production by Spencer Rosio
Originated by Capstone Global Library Ltd
Printed and bound in India
PO1020

978 1 3982 0114 9 (hardback)
978 1 3982 0116 3 (paperback)

British Library Cataloguing in Publication Data
A full catalogue record for this book is available from the British Library.

Acknowledgements
We would like to thank the following for permission to reproduce photographs: Cover: Shutterstock: Vitchanan Photography; Inside: Shutterstock: Andrey Popov 9, Arena Creative 21, Tad Denson 38, DGLimages 37, Dragon Images 13, Dean Drobot 44, Easy Camera 34, ESB Professional 18, Iakov Filimonov 19, 26, Firma V 42, GaudiLab 31, India Picture 33, Inked Pixels 30, Italika 14, Karelnoppe 35, Lopolo 16, Rob Marmion 25, Mimagephotography 40, Monkey Business Images 7, 20, 45, El Nariz 32, Oliveromg 6, William Perugini 27, Photographee.eu 8, Pjcross 23, Rawpixel.com 5, 29, SpeedKingz 4, 28, 39, Syda Productions 22, 41, The palms 43, Tommaso79 1, 12, Suzanne Tucker 24, Yakobchuk Viacheslav 36, Visualpower 11, Vitchanan Photography 10, Tracy Whiteside 17, Yuyi 15.

Every effort has been made to contact copyright holders of material reproduced in this book. Any omissions will be rectified in subsequent printings if notice is given to the publisher.

Contents

Chapter 1
What is bullying?

Bullying comes in many forms, but essentially it is when someone does something to hurt, scare or **threaten** another person on purpose, time and again. Most of us have seen bullying or have had the misfortune to experience bullying at some time in our lives. Examples of bullying are when someone keeps on pushing another child around, stealing their lunch money or insulting and teasing them when they walk past.

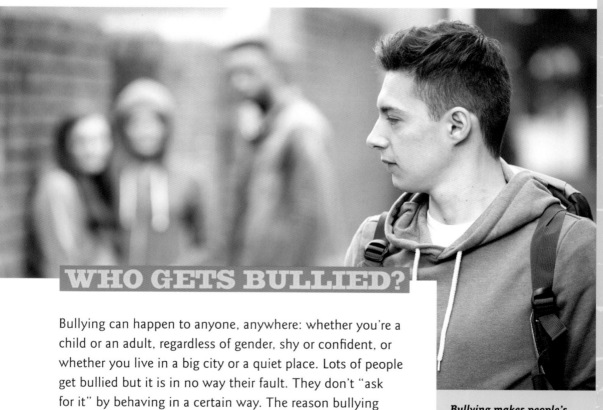

WHO GETS BULLIED?

Bullying can happen to anyone, anywhere: whether you're a child or an adult, regardless of gender, shy or confident, or whether you live in a big city or a quiet place. Lots of people get bullied but it is in no way their fault. They don't "ask for it" by behaving in a certain way. The reason bullying happens is all about the bully. Children who bully use what they think is their power to upset or control others. They may be bigger or stronger, or more popular, or know a secret about someone.

Bullying makes people's lives miserable.

WHY BULLYING IS SO SERIOUS

When a friend is in a bad mood and calls you a name, that is not necessarily bullying. If someone pushes you accidentally on the sports field, that one incident does not count as bullying either. Bullying is when someone intends to hurt you, and either keeps on doing it or intends to keep on doing it. If someone hurts you by accident it is annoying and they should say sorry but it does not make them a bully. If a friend is mean they should apologize too but if it doesn't happen again and again then hopefully it can be resolved. Bullies are consistently aggressive and repeatedly do things to hurt someone else. That is what makes bullying so painful and so serious.

Bullying can happen to anyone but true friends can help you through it.

Types of bullying

There are three main types of bullying. Verbal bullying is when a bully says or writes mean things to or about someone else. It can include name-calling, taunting and threatening. A lot of the bullying that goes on in school is in this form. There is also relationship or social bullying. This happens when a bully or group of bullies excludes someone on purpose, tells other people not to be friends with them, spreads **rumours** about them or does or says things that embarrass them in public, like revealing a secret they have been told. The third type is physical bullying, when a bully hurts someone by doing something like hitting, kicking or pushing them, or when they take or break their possessions.

Physical bullying is when a bully or a group of bullies hurts someone's body or damages their belongings.

BULLYING AND PREJUDICE

Bullies bully all kinds of people for many different reasons but unfortunately some groups of people may be at an increased risk of being bullied because bullies see them as different in some way. Some bullies who feel a need to be mean and destructive target people who are more obviously different to themselves, such as **lesbian**, **gay**, **bisexual** or **transgender** (LGBT) young people or people with disabilities. They may target **refugees** or others who they think are outsiders in some way. When someone bullies another person because of their **race**, **sexuality**, religion or **culture** it is called **prejudice**. Bullies also sometimes target people they think look weak or unlikely to fight back, or people who look nervous or have low **self-esteem** already.

Children and young people with disabilities or with special health needs may be at higher risk of being bullied.

Not every child who identifies as, for example, transgender, will necessarily be bullied but they are more likely to be a target. The important thing to remember is that the victim is in no way to blame for the bullying. The problem is always the bully and their bullying behaviour.

Bullying matters

Bullying matters because it can affect people badly. Bullying can make people feel scared, upset and alone. It makes some people feel angry, and even violent. It can stop them from sleeping at night, make them lose their appetite and even make some people physically ill. Some will start to skip classes or whole school days so they can avoid the bullies. This makes them fall behind with school work and get into trouble with teachers, and maybe do less well in school than they deserve to. Some children even harm themselves because they are being bullied.

TURNING THINGS AROUND

Bullying also affects people's self-esteem, their sense of self-worth. They can lose confidence and start to think that in some way it is their fault, that they are all alone, that there is nothing they can do about it and that no one will understand how they feel. If the bullying happens at school or near their home, they can feel that there is no escape. In fact, there are many things you can do to tackle bullies and their bullying. Many people have been bullied and come through it. Bullying is a dangerous and nasty business, but it can be stopped. Victims need to trust that there will be happier times ahead.

When you are in trouble you need to be with the people who care about you and who are willing to understand how you feel.

Skills for life

If you are being bullied, it is so important to remember that you are not alone. There are many people who care about you and can help you. There are things you can do to have the bullying shut down and there are tactics to help you survive until it is over. One thing you can do is read books like this and talk about the issues with your friends. Do not let bullies hide behind a veil of secrecy. Deciding to do something about bullying is the first step to sorting it out.

People who are bullied often feel alone. In fact there are many people who are bullied and feel as they do. If you are being bullied you need to tell someone what is happening and you won't feel so alone any more.

Chapter 2

Beat the bullies

Bullies use verbal, physical and relationship, or social, bullying in different ways. It can help to know when teasing becomes bullying, or when a friend crosses a line and becomes a bully. Identifying bullying is important.

Name-calling is a very painful type of bullying.

BULLYING IS NOT FUNNY

When someone is teased, taunted or insulted regularly, this is bullying. A bully might make comments about the way a person looks, insult them about their lack of sporting skills or mock them for their grades. When they are asked about their bullying behaviour, some bullies try to make it seem like they were just being funny or making a joke and that the insult was harmless. They try to make it the victim's problem for not being able to take a joke. Hurting someone's feelings is never harmless and it's not a joke. It's bullying. One way to tell the difference is to check how you feel. When a friend teases you, you probably laugh. When a bully teases you, it makes you feel scared, upset, embarrassed or hurt. No one has the right to make you feel like this.

If a friend calls you a name that hurts your feelings but they intended it as a joke and did not mean any harm, tell them how you feel. This can work with some bullies too. Try not to shout or sound too upset when you talk to them. Try to keep a calm, confident voice. Tell them that you do not like being called names and that you would like them to stop. If they laugh and say you can't take a joke, ask them again to stop. Tell them it's not unreasonable to not want to be insulted.

However it happens, being called names or being insulted can have a damaging effect on your wellbeing and it must be stopped.

Finding true friends

When a bully messes with your friendships, this can be really upsetting. An example of relationship bullying is when someone invites everyone in the class except you to a party. Another is when they find reasons to exclude you from games. When people who you thought were friends start whispering about you behind your back or start going quiet when you walk by as if they are talking about you, that is also bullying. Relationship bullying like this can make people feel left out and lonely, as if nobody likes them. This can be really hurtful and damaging.

EXPLAIN HOW YOU FEEL

What is especially nasty about relationship bullying is that while it may be started by one person, other people join in or let it happen. It can feel as if people you thought were friends now dislike you. The truth is that even nice people can make mistakes sometimes, and sometimes they go along with the bullying because they are scared that if they don't it will happen to them. Try to talk to your friends. Explain how you are feeling. Maybe they did not realize the **impact** their behaviour was having. Once you explain, they may help you to make it stop.

Being left out by people you thought were friends is upsetting because you feel betrayed and alone.

People who hurt you regularly are not true friends. Real friends are those who are always there for you and always stick up for you and support you.

MAKING NEW FRIENDS

If people you thought were your friends keep on being mean, then they are not true friends. Hard though this may be, it is probably time to make some new, true friends. Real friends will support you and be there for you. There are lots of ways to find new friends. You could join a new club or take up a new sport. Or you can just try chatting to someone new around school about random things, such as clothes, or what films or music they like. Don't worry if you don't make new friends straight away. It can take time, but if you are friendly and open you will be surprised how well people react.

Safety first

In physical bullying, the main weapon the bully uses is their body. They might shove, punch or kick someone, or they might damage someone else's stuff. Sometimes the physical bully leaves their victim with cuts, bruises or other injuries. Often, though, physical bullying includes things like pulling someone's hair or clothes or pinching or pushing them. This may not leave marks that anyone can see, but it is still physical bullying and it must be stopped.

UNDER THREAT

Physical bullying can happen even if someone does not touch you at all. If a bully threatens to hurt you, that threat is a serious form of bullying. Even if you think the bully is unlikely to carry out their threats, they may still be dangerous. You need to put safety first and tell a parent, teacher or other adult about the threat so they can deal with it immediately.

If someone threatens to hit you this is still bullying and must be reported, even if they don't actually touch you.

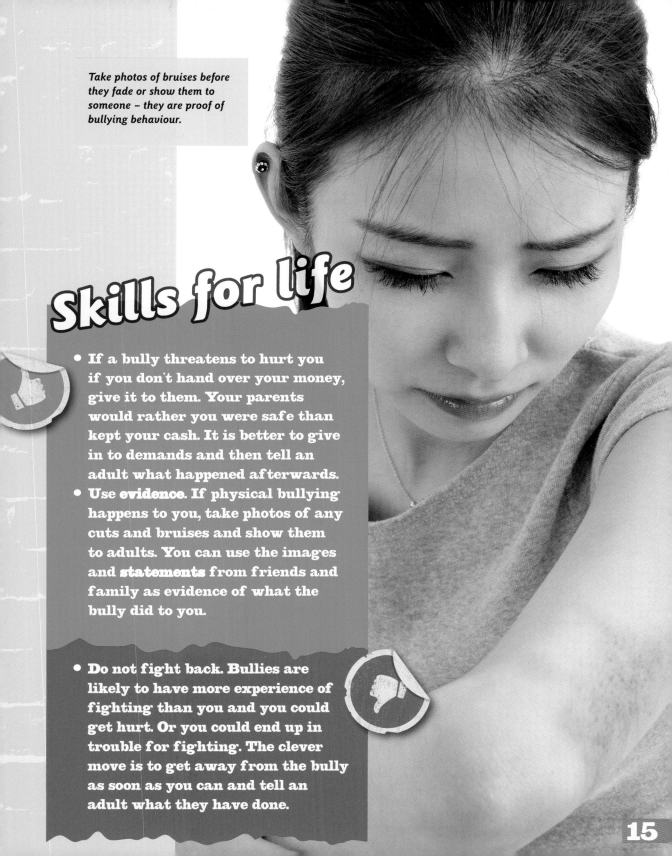

Take photos of bruises before they fade or show them to someone – they are proof of bullying behaviour.

Skills for life

- If a bully threatens to hurt you if you don't hand over your money, give it to them. Your parents would rather you were safe than kept your cash. It is better to give in to demands and then tell an adult what happened afterwards.

- Use **evidence**. If physical bullying happens to you, take photos of any cuts and bruises and show them to adults. You can use the images and **statements** from friends and family as evidence of what the bully did to you.

- Do not fight back. Bullies are likely to have more experience of fighting than you and you could get hurt. Or you could end up in trouble for fighting. The clever move is to get away from the bully as soon as you can and tell an adult what they have done.

Chapter 3
Adult bullies

Bullies are usually around the same age as their targets. So, if bullying happens at school, the chances are that the bully and the person who is being bullied are in the same class or year. Sometimes, however, adults can be bullies too. While most of the parents, teachers, coaches and other adults you meet are kind, caring and want what is best for you, occasionally some adults' behaviour can be classed as bullying.

PARENT PROBLEMS

Most parents shout or get angry sometimes. Often it may be that their children have done something to deserve it. It is not bullying if a parent tells you off for not doing your chores again and again, for example. Most parents only get cross because they care about their children and want them to be the best they can be. But a parent who bullies is someone who **abuses** their child in some way. They might insult them all the time, calling them names and making them feel stupid or useless. Some parent bullies even hit, or threaten to hit, their children.

Parents should protect you from bullies but some parents become bullies themselves.

It is hard to tell on someone you love even though they hurt you, but you must seek help, for both your sakes.

WHAT SHOULD YOU DO?

Dealing with a parent who is a bully is really hard. After all, it is your parents you would usually turn to for help with a problem like this. The first thing to do is explain to them how their behaviour is making you feel. They may not realize how you feel. Perhaps they only intended to encourage you to work harder at school when they were actually making you feel bad about yourself, for example. Maybe they were having problems of their own, say at work, and were taking them out on you. Everyone makes mistakes, so simply explaining the problem calmly might help. If it does not, think about who else you can talk to. Is there someone else in the family you trust? If not, try telling your teacher or doctor.

Teacher troubles

It might make you feel embarrassed, hurt or angry when a teacher tells you off in front of your whole class or punishes you for doing something wrong, but this is not necessarily bullying. It is a teacher's job to keep their class under control and to ensure that their students do their work on time and try their best. They do this to help students achieve good results and learn the correct way to behave in certain situations. Sometimes, though, a teacher uses their position of power in a negative way, and this becomes bullying.

Every student has the right to be treated fairly and kindly and bullying and threatening behaviour from the teacher should not be happening.

WHAT IS TEACHER BULLYING?

A teacher is a bully if they regularly pick on one student, criticizing them and putting them down, often for no reason. Perhaps they make fun of that student, mocking them for their poor work, race, personality or appearance, and making the rest of the class laugh at them. Or they could consistently grade their work lower than the student truly feels they deserve. Some teachers may even threaten to hit their students.

Bullying by anyone is bad and must be stopped. When a teacher is a bully, this can make other students think that this is an acceptable way to treat people, even if they really know that it is not. The first thing to do is ask yourself if you behave well in class and do your homework on time. Remove any excuses that the teacher might have for criticizing you. Then, talk to your parents. Explain what is happening, and ask them to talk to the teacher. Your parents should speak to the headteacher of your school and possibly the board of governors until something is done to stop the bullying.

Telling your parents or another trusted adult is the only way to sort out the problem of a teacher bully.

Coaching the coaches

It can get pretty intense on a sports pitch. Emotions run high, especially during important games or matches in a competition. Sports coaches are often seen on the sidelines, shouting to their players to run faster, work harder, focus better. Tough, challenging coaching is about positively pushing a player out of his or her comfort zone to make them perform better. Coaches demand focus and effort every day, during practice as well as in a competition. Sometimes a coach may tease or say something slightly mean to a player to make them work harder, but they must be careful not to cross a line and become a bully.

Coaches should be supportive and encouraging, not bullying.

BEHAVIOUR THAT BACKFIRES

Some people think that bullying behaviour by coaches is **motivational**. They think that shouting at someone or calling them a failure will make them work harder. But if a coach is constantly calling the players on their team rude or mean names, that becomes bullying. If a coach always yells at their players, they are a bully. If a coach constantly **belittles** or insults players, they are a bully. When a coach is a bully, they can make a child hate a sport they used to love. It can make them so unhappy that it affects their life more generally. It is damaging to children, and it also produces worse results on the sports field.

Skills for life

- Do talk to your parents or another adult you can trust about any coach who is a bully.
- Do get proof. Perhaps parents could video the behaviour during practice or a match.
- Do ask your parents to talk to the coach.

- Don't do nothing. Be brave and say something.
- Don't keep it secret. Tell other players. They may feel the same or may have noticed the coach bullying you.
- Don't give up. If nothing changes after your parents have spoken to the coach, ask them to contact the authorities.

Bullying tactics have no place in youth sports and do more to damage than to motivate athletes.

Chapter 4
Are you a bully?

Bullying does not only affect the victim. Bullying is bad for the bullies too. Both the people who get bullied and the children who are bullies can be left with serious, long-lasting problems. Understanding the different reasons why some people become bullies can help both groups.

BULLIES WHO HAVE BEEN BULLIED

Very often, bullies are people who have been bullied themselves. A bully may be someone who has a hard time at home and does not feel loved or cared for by their family. When someone is bullied, shouted at constantly, or even hurt at home they may take out their anger and **frustration** by bullying someone at school. They are repeating ways of behaviour that they have learned. Sometimes they bully others as a way to get attention for their own suffering.

The vast majority of bullies are victims of bullying themselves.

Some people bully because they lack self-confidence or self-esteem. They may seem confident and loud but actually they do not feel very powerful. By bullying someone they perceive as weaker than themselves, they try to look more powerful and confident. Other bullies may feel they do not have many friends. Getting a laugh at someone else's expense makes them feel better, and getting other people to join with them makes them feel more popular.

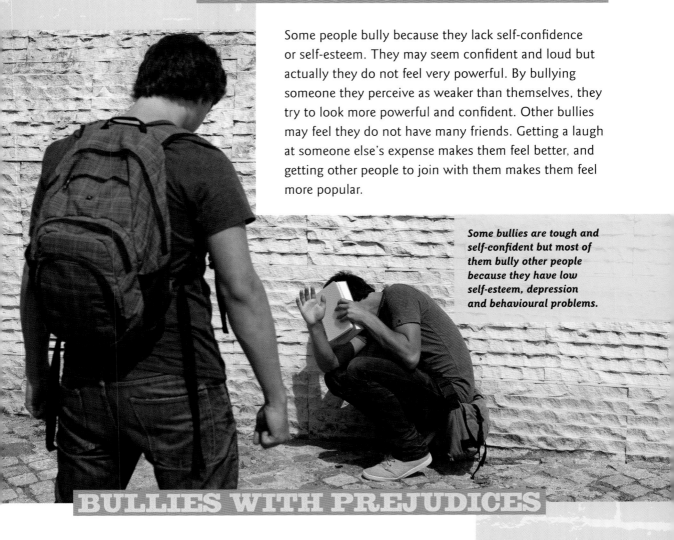

Some bullies are tough and self-confident but most of them bully other people because they have low self-esteem, depression and behavioural problems.

BULLIES WITH PREJUDICES

Some bullies pick on people of a different race, religion or sexual orientation because they are **racist** or **homophobic**. That means they are prejudiced against people from a different culture, nationality or background, or because they are gay or lesbian. These attitudes are dangerous and unfair. Prejudice is when someone has a negative opinion about a whole group of people. You cannot judge someone from a particular group without even knowing them. Disliking an individual before you have spoken to them, or know anything about them, is totally unjust and unfair.

Think before you act

If you have bullied or are bullying other people how can you stop? The first thing to do is to figure out why you do it. What is the cause of the problem? Do you bully others because you are unhappy about something? If so, focus on sorting out that aspect of your life so you can be happier. Are you bullying because others in your group are doing it and you do not want them to reject you? Maybe you need to get a different group of friends, who appreciate you for who you are rather than make you behave badly.

If you've been a bully in the past you don't have to be a bully any more. Think about how you can change.

WHAT LEADS TO THE BULLYING?

What goes through your head when you are bullying someone? Are there particular events that lead to the bullying? For example, if having trouble with homework makes you bully someone clever, you could ask for extra help to get on top of your own work and to avoid this trigger. Sometimes people bully someone who was once their friend because they are hurt about the way that friend treated them or a misunderstanding has broken up their friendship. In this case, try talking to that person instead, to clear up the misunderstanding or to release your anger. Tell them calmly how you feel rather than letting your frustration turn you into a bully.

Take the first step – say NO to bullying.

BULLYING

TAKE CONTROL

It is important to accept that even if there are reasons why a person bullies, they still have power over their own actions. They make the decisions that cause them to behave in a bad way, and they need to take control of that behaviour. This means thinking about how and why they behave in a certain way and changing it. So, for example, if a bully knows they are more likely to bully someone they dislike, they should avoid that person. Or if they are more likely to bully when they feel angry, they should find ways to deal with their anger, such as counting slowly to ten before they speak. If they cannot make the change by themselves, they should talk to a **counsellor** or teacher about how to change their behaviour.

A new you

Bullying can seriously affect the victim's life, but it can also seriously affect a bully's life. Bullies can end up getting **suspended** or **expelled** from school or even arrested in certain circumstances. If you are a bully, it is time to take control and be a new you.

Think about how bullying would affect a friend you care about. Why would you want anyone to feel bad like that?

THINK ABOUT HOW BULLYING AFFECTS OTHERS

Take time out to really think about how your behaviour affects the people you bully. Put yourself in the victim's position. How would you feel if you had to go to school every day knowing someone there was going to hurt you physically or emotionally? We should all treat others how we would want to be treated. Are you aware of how damaging bullying can be? If you have been bullied yourself, you will know very well. Victims of bullying can become bullies or criminals later in life, and some even commit **suicide**. If you're a bully, can you imagine how awful you would feel to have that on your conscience?

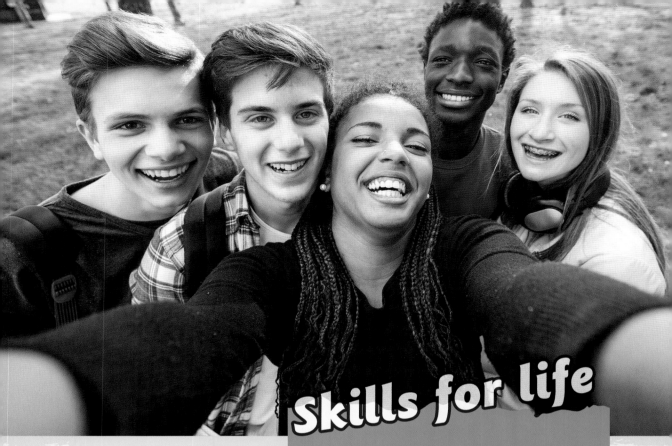

Skills for life

Find new ways of understanding and getting along with people and leave bullying behind.

You might even choose to apologize to the people you have hurt. This takes a lot of courage but it might help you to regain other people's trust and you will feel better. If you do apologize, make sure the apology is sincere and take full responsibility for the wrongdoing.

Try to become more positive about yourself and others. Find things to like in other people and yourself, rather than focusing on the bad points. Spend time with people and get to know them better, and you will probably find you have something in common and something to like about them. If you pick on people because of their differences, try to find the things you have in common, as well as appreciating what makes everyone unique. If you bully people to make other people laugh and to feel more popular, try instead to be kind to other people. You will find you make more and truer friends that way.

Chapter 5

Cyberbullying

Cyberbullying is when bullies use technology to send mean and rude messages to or about another person (or people), with the intention of making them feel embarrassed or bad. Cyberbullies may also use technology to harass or threaten another person. Cyberbullying can be devastating, because victims feel they have no escape from it. Before the days of the internet and social media, people who were bullied at school could at least feel safe when they got home. Today, victims of cyberbullying face constant stress. Many of us use our mobile phones, tablets and computers all the time, meaning that once bullies get access to someone online they can target them day and night.

WHY ARE CYBERBULLIES SO MEAN?

The other thing that is horrible about cyberbullying is that it is often **anonymous**. The target of the bullying may not know who sent that mean text or who posted that embarrassing photo. This can make cyberbullies lose control. They cannot see the effects of their bullying on other people as they would if they were bullying at school, so they become even meaner online. They feel they are safe online and less likely to be caught.

Cyberbullying can make life miserable for the victim 24/7.

Using technology to make people laugh at someone is just as bad as bullying them in person.

THE TRUTH IS OUT THERE

As cyberbullying can be anonymous, it can seem harder to get evidence about cyberbullies. Even if cyberbullies use false names, everything that is posted on the internet stays there, even if someone deletes it. When a file has been uploaded it goes onto a **server** so it can be viewed later, and it stays on the server. So, if a bully posts mean or rude messages or images online, someone will be able to find it and use it as evidence. For a bully, the other danger is that in the future, when you have grown up and stopped being a bully, an employer will be able to see your activity when you apply for a job. Your behaviour will be a concern and could stop you from getting that and other jobs.

Master mobile phone bullies

When a mobile phone buzzes or rings to say a message has arrived or a call is coming in, most of us pick it up eagerly. If someone is being cyberbullied, they have a totally different reaction. They fear that when they open the message it will have threatening or abusive content, or when they answer it may be someone calling them names or threatening to hurt them. Sometimes the **impersonal** nature of instant messaging can make us think someone is being mean, when actually they intend to make a joke. It is tricky to detect the sender's intended tone when you cannot see their face. Cyberbullying is when someone keeps sending messages or images with the intention of hurting, scaring or upsetting you.

Don't leave mobile phones unattended. A bully might get your number from it or use it to send fake messages from you to get you into trouble.

THINGS TO DO

There are some basic things you can do to protect your phone and reduce the chances of a bully being able to reach you. First, only give out your phone number to friends and family you trust, and ask them not to pass it on without your permission. Next, only answer calls from people you know. Never answer a call from a withheld number or reply to a text or other message from someone you don't know.

Avoid answering calls from unknown numbers or from someone you know is a bully.

If a bully gets your number, do not reply to anything they send you. They may think you are not getting the messages and give up. At the very least they will not know how they are affecting you. Next, block their number. You should be able to do this on your phone, but if not, contact your phone company to do it. If necessary, get a replacement SIM card. Tell your parents about the bullying so that they can tell the school if it is someone you know or the phone company. Phone companies can **trace** the number of someone who sends abusive messages.

Intercept the internet nasties

Bullies use the internet to hurt people in different ways. They may send insulting emails, messages or tweets, or give a harsh or cruel response to a status update on Facebook. Sometimes they bully people in chatrooms or even impersonate a victim online. To do this they might post personal information, photos or videos designed to embarrass another person on a fake personal page.

KEEP SAFE

Keep safe by being careful not to give out personal information when you are chatting or posting online. This means things like your email address, phone number and passwords. Never give out any of these personal things (including your home address) to anyone who is not already a friend or a member of your family. Do not reply to unpleasant emails or postings in chatrooms, and use a fake name in any situation where people you don't know might be able to contact you. That way they will not be able to track you down. If you are bullied by one or more people in a chatroom, leave it. Set up private chatrooms or groups where only you and people who are already your friends can join in.

Using computers and going online should be a positive experience. Do not let cyberbullies spoil your fun.

Skills for life

- If you experience an incident of cyberbullying online, log off that page or site straight away.

- Print and/or save copies of any incidents of bullying that you can, such as nasty emails or offensive images.

- Tell your parents about the bullying.

- Together, contact your service provider about the bullying.

- Use blocking software to keep bullies out.

- Change your passwords and screen name and start to use the internet safely again.

Don't put off telling your parents out of fear that they might stop you from using the computer. It is more important to stop the bullying.

Safety on social networks

Many people use social networking sites like Facebook, Instagram, Twitter, Snapchat or Tumblr every day. These are sites where people can discuss things like music and news, post images and articles about themselves and comment on other people's **profiles**. They can be great fun but they can also be a place for cyberbullies to act.

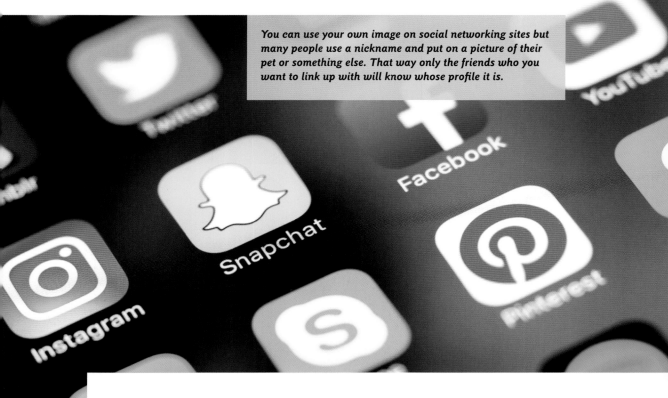

You can use your own image on social networking sites but many people use a nickname and put on a picture of their pet or something else. That way only the friends who you want to link up with will know whose profile it is.

A cyberbully could **hack** into a person's account and post nasty pictures to make it look like they did it or to embarrass them. Some cyberbullies post insulting or hurtful messages on other people's profile pages or put unpleasant images of someone on their own page and link it to all their friends to humiliate a victim.

Keep your social media settings on private so that only friends see your posts and photos.

BE SMART

When you open a page or profile on a social networking site, use privacy settings from the very start so you can control who sees your posts and who can contact you. Be careful what you post. Do not include pictures or tell secrets that you would not want everyone to see. It is easy for bullies to find information online, and they might use these things against you. If you are on a social networking site and someone you don't know asks to friend you, say no. Someone online might lie about who they are, so unless you know them already and trust them, do not friend them, however nice or sincere they might seem. It is too risky.

Tell your parent, caregiver or a trusted adult if anyone or anything makes you feel uncomfortable or worried, or if you or someone you know is being bullied online. The punishment for cyberbullies can include being suspended or even expelled from school, and certain types of cyberbullying are considered crimes.

Chapter 6

Survival guide

Bullies are the only ones to blame for bullying and the bullying is 100 per cent their responsibility. However, there are some strategies you can use that can take some of the sting out of the different ways that bullies act, and the way they make you feel. The very first, and most important, thing you must do is tell someone what is happening.

TELL SOMEONE

Some people try to deal with bullying themselves. They think that if they tell someone they might not be taken seriously or that it might make the bullying worse. They worry that they will be teased for "snitching". All kinds of bullying are serious and damaging and must be stopped. Every one of us has the right to feel safe and respected. Keeping quiet about bullying only lets the bully win. If you are being picked on at school, it is so important to tell someone. Telling someone about bullying is actually very brave. If you report a bully, you are helping not only yourself but other people too; people who may be bullied now and in the future.

If the first person you tell is not helpful, try someone new. Don't give up. All adults should take bullying very seriously. You will find someone who will help.

You could keep a diary of bullying incidents to show a teacher, as evidence of what has happened.

WHO SHOULD I TELL?

Ideally, tell your parents. If you are being bullied, they will probably have noticed a change in your behaviour and may be worried about you already. They will be able to help you deal with it and tell other people. Tell a teacher if the bullying happens in school, or a coach or club leader if it happens in one of those settings. Telling a person of authority should mean they can act on the information immediately. They may be able to find a way to sort out the problem: for example, by having a general talk about bullying and the consequences for any bullies who are caught without the bully even knowing who reported them.

Make tracks!

Telling someone about the bullying to get it stopped is priority number one. In the meantime, one tactic you can use to limit the bully's power is to ignore them. Hide your true reactions and walk on by. Imagine that the words they are saying are just noise or the buzzing of a bee, and blank them out. A bully wants to see a reaction from you, to see you angry or upset. By hiding your reactions, you rob them of this pleasure. Of course, it's hard to ignore an insult, but remind yourself that just because a bully says something it doesn't mean anyone else believes it.

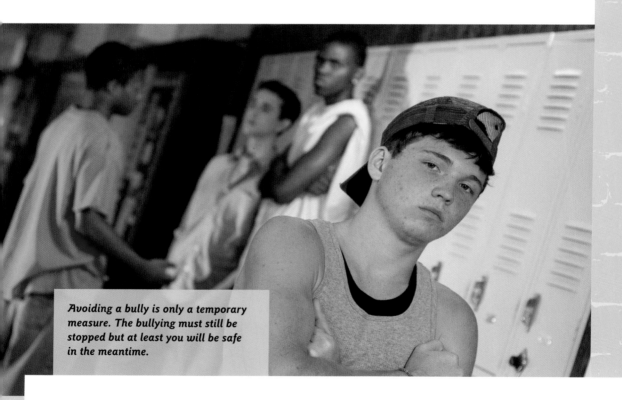

Avoiding a bully is only a temporary measure. The bullying must still be stopped but at least you will be safe in the meantime.

You could try slow, deep breathing and focus when you walk away, rather than thinking about what the bully just said. Or, practice different ways of reacting before the bullying happens, so you are prepared. Either avoid eye contact with the bully or try to look at them as if you don't care about what they said. If you are lucky, they will become bored with your lack of response and stop annoying you.

Ignoring a bully is not the same as ignoring the bullying. You must still tell someone it is happening as soon as you can.

AVOID DANGER

Nobody should have to change their life in any way because of a bully but you have to be safe. While the bullying is being dealt with, you might choose to avoid situations that bring you face to face with the bully. This could be as simple as moving chairs in class or avoiding quiet corners of the playground where bullying can happen out of sight of the teachers. You could go to the toilets with a friend and avoid hanging around by the school gates alone at the end of the day.

Be the comeback king or queen

A different strategy that some people use against bullies is to answer them back and turn the tables on them. When an insult makes you feel sad or angry, instead of ignoring it you can try making a joke of it instead. If you can twist a bully's words to make a funny reply, the people the bully is showing off to may laugh at your joke instead of what the bully's doing. Sometimes it can be as simple as twisting a comment to take the sting out of it. For example, if they say a mean thing about your outfit say, "Well, I like it," or if they insult your hairstyle say, "Yeah, I didn't have time to brush it today". A bully may leave you alone if you don't let them have the last word.

Making people laugh about a bully's taunts can be a useful defence.

BE DIRECT

Clever comebacks can be hard to do, and sometimes a direct response is just as effective. Using a firm and loud voice (though not shouting) say something like "That's a horrible thing to say. Why would you say that?" or "Don't speak to me like that, please. It's unfair and I don't like it". Try to speak clearly and calmly, as if you are in control. Try not to raise your voice or start arguing with what the bully said. You don't want to be drawn into a fight. You do not have to explain why it's unfair or why you don't like what they said.

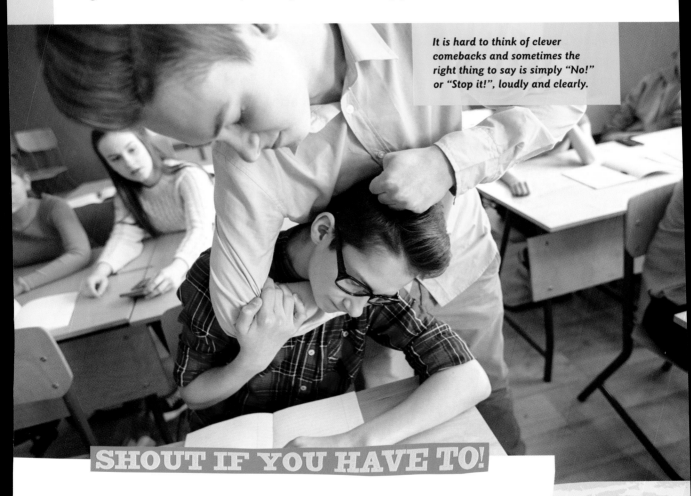

It is hard to think of clever comebacks and sometimes the right thing to say is simply "No!" or "Stop it!", loudly and clearly.

SHOUT IF YOU HAVE TO!

If a bully hits or hurts you, you should not keep calm. Now is the time to raise your voice! Shout "Stop it!" or "You're hurting me!" loud and clear, for all to hear. The bully will probably let you go and leave, in case a teacher comes along to see what is happening.

Give yourself a boost

Bullies can hurt your confidence and make you feel bad. Mean comments can undermine your self-esteem and make you feel low. One way to survive bullying is to build your confidence back up again. You have so much going for you. You just need to remind yourself of that. Write down a list of your good points. Ask your friends and family to compliment you. Take up a new hobby or take more time to do the things you know you are or could be good at. The positive feedback you get and the buzz you feel from doing something well will show you that you have a lot to be proud of.

Writing down a list of your good points and the positive things in your life can help make you feel better.

FAKE IT TILL YOU MAKE IT

The other thing about feeling more confident is that you will look more confident. People who look more confident might be bothered less by bullies. Bullies often target people who look **vulnerable** or quiet or nervous, perhaps because the bully thinks they will be less likely to answer back or speak up. If you can act confident and determined, even if you don't actually feel it, bullies are more likely to leave you alone.

Skills for life

To appear more confident, hold your head up high and walk straight and tall. Try not to look at the ground, shuffle along or keep checking your phone. You could practise in front of a mirror or with a family member or good friend. This could make you laugh and help you to feel you can do it. If you can fake confidence for a while, say a month, you will find you are walking taller without even thinking about it!

When things are getting you down, take time to remind yourself of the good stuff and do things that make you feel good about yourself.

Take a stand!

Bullying does not only hurt the target of the bullying. It hurts the bully and the people who see it happening. Bullying can make the people watching it feel uncomfortable and scared too. That is why it is not just the responsibility of the person who is being bullied to tell adults about it. We should all be aware of what bullying is, what it looks like and how it makes people feel. We should all take a stand and help to stop bullying.

STRENGTH IN NUMBERS

Some people who are bullied feel like no one cares or even notices what they are going through. If you see someone being bullied, go up to them and ask if they are OK and if there is anything you can do to help. Perhaps you could ask them to sit with you at lunch or join in with whatever you are doing. You can wait until the bully has left if you are scared. Knowing another person is taking notice will help the victim feel less isolated. If your friend is being bullied, stand by them. There is strength in numbers. Walk with them in a group to classes and together show the bully that the victim is not alone.

Bullies tend to give up when other kids do not support their behaviour.

Telling a teacher about bullying means they can take a stand and make a bully stop.

Skills for Life

We should all make sure that we never join in with a bully's laughter or name-calling, never watch or smile when a bully is targeting someone and never stand by and let it continue. If everyone, children and adults, took a stand there would be fewer bullies in the world.

Do not put yourself at risk. If a bully is scary or dangerous or you are worried about becoming a victim yourself, don't speak to them. Go straight to a teacher or another adult and tell them about the bullying you have witnessed. This is especially important if there is a fight. You only risk getting hurt yourself if you try to get involved. It is better to run and get a teacher to stop the fighting.

Glossary

abuse when someone is treated with cruelty or violence, especially regularly or repeatedly

anonymous when the person responsible is not named or identified

belittle try to make someone feel unimportant

bisexual someone who is sexually attracted to both men and women

counsellor a person who is trained to give advice and help people with their problems

culture a particular society that has its own beliefs and ways of life

evidence proof that something has happened

expelled banned from attending a school

frustration the feeling of being upset or annoyed when you cannot change or achieve something

gay attracted to people of the same sex

hack to gain access to someone else's computer files without their permission

homophobic prejudiced against people who are gay or homosexual

impact an effect on someone or something

impersonal not referring to or done by an identifiable person

lesbian a woman who is sexually attracted to other women

motivational something that encourages or persuades someone to do something

prejudice an unfair and unreasonable opinion or feeling towards a person because of what group they belong to

profile display of personal facts linked with a specific computer user

race a group of people sharing the same physical characteristics such as skin colour and features, and often the same culture and history

racist prejudiced against people from a particular race

refugee person who leaves their home or country because of danger in order to find somewhere to live where they can be safe

rumour story that people pass between each other about someone, usually negative

self-esteem self-confidence; having a positive view of oneself

server a computer or computer program which manages access to a central resource or service in a network

sexuality one's sexuality is defined by whether they find people of the same or a different sex attractive

statement report of what someone has said or witnessed

suicide killing oneself deliberately

suspended banned from a school for a period of time as punishment

threaten when someone says they will hurt another person or do something unpleasant or unkind to them, often in order to make someone do what they want

trace track down

transgender someone whose personal identity is different from their assigned birth gender, so someone who was thought to be female at birth might identify as a boy

vulnerable able to be easily physically, emotionally or mentally hurt

Find out more

BOOKS

Be Bully Free: A Hands-On Guide to How You Can Take Control, Michael Panckridge and Catherine Thornton (Jessica Kingsley Publishers, 2017)

Cyberbullying (Tech Safety Tips), Heather E. Schwartz (Raintree, 2017)

How to Handle Bullying and Gangs (Under Pressure), Honor Head (Franklin Watts, 2014)

Mobile Phone Safety (Tech Safety Tips), Kathy Allen (Raintree, 2017)

WEBSITES

Childline
childline.org.uk
Childline's counsellors offer support for children under 19 years old either online or on the phone 24 hours a day, 7 days a week.

The Mix
themix.org.uk
The Mix offers advice about issues such as coming out and mental health.

Young Minds
youngminds.org.uk
Young Minds is a leading charity fighting for children and young people's mental health.

Note to parents and teachers: the Publishers have made every effort to recommend websites that are from trustworthy sources and that are age-appropriate for the readers of this book. However, due to the changing nature of the internet, we cannot be responsible for content shown on these pages and we recommend that all websites are viewed under the supervision of a responsible adult.

Index